P9-EMM-914

For
Ron
and
Cecily
and
Renée
and
Dan,
too

illustrated by Richard Powers

ANNE K. ROSE

SAMSON and DELILAH

Lothrop, Lee & Shepard Co., Inc., New York

Library of Congress Catalog Card No.: 68-27713 · Printed in the U.S.A.
1 2 3 4 5 72 71 70 69 68

Samson was born in Israel long ago when the Philistines ruled the land.

Before Samson's birth an angel visited his mother and told her that the child would grow up to deliver the people of Israel from the cruel Philistines. But she must never allow Samson's hair to be cut, the angel warned.

From boyhood Samson was strong, quick-moving, and handsome. He had large eyes and dark-gold hair which hung to his shoulders, for it had never been cut. As he grew older, his strength grew with him. By the time he was fully grown, no one in all Israel was stronger.

Once, roaming in the mountains, Samson was startled by a terrible roar. There, in the path before him, crouched a huge lion. Samson was not afraid. With his bare hands he fell upon the beast, tore it to bits, and flung the carcass to the ground.

At this time in his life and against his parents' wishes, Samson chose a Philistine woman to be his wife. Later she was taken away from him.

A great anger came over Samson, who felt the whole land was a prison. He decided to take revenge on all the Philistines. Samson caught three hundred foxes in the mountains and tied them together by their tails, two at a time. Then he set fire to their tails and let them run loose in the fields of the

Philistines. Maddened with pain, the foxes ran with their fiery tails through the vineyards and olive groves and fields of corn, setting fire to the crops and burning them.

When the Philistines saw their burning fields and vineyards, they were filled with rage. Quickly they found out who had done it. To punish Samson they seized his wife and her father and burned them.

Samson roared with anguish. "Though you have done this," he cried, "I will be avenged yet!" He took up his sword and fought the Philistines, leaving many dead. Then he went off to live among the hills.

The Philistines turned in fury against Israel then. Their wrath caused much woe throughout the land, and the people knew fear as never before. At last the men of Israel, three thousand strong, stormed into the mountains to find Samson.

"What have you done to us, your own people?" they demanded. "Have you forgotten the Philistines rule over us?"

Samson said, "As they have done to me, so have I done to them."

"We live in fear and tremble for our lives," the men of Israel said. "So we have come to deliver you into the hands of the Philistines."

Sure of his own strength, Samson agreed. "Carry me to them as your prisoner," he said, "but promise me you will not fall upon me yourselves."

The men of Israel bound Samson with new cords then and led him into the camp of the Philistines. When the Philistines saw him a great shout went up. They jeered at Samson and taunted him until, bursting with anger, he broke out of the ropes that fastened him. With a fierce cry, he seized the jawbone of an ass and attacked his enemies.

One after another, the Philistines fell beneath his fearful blows. At last Samson looked down at the dead that lay before him, and thundered, "With the jawbone of an ass I have slain a thousand men!"

The battle had ended and a great stillness spread over the plain. "Water!" cried Samson. Through parched lips he called upon God. "And now shall I die of thirst?"

At that moment his glance fell upon the jawbone he had cast aside. A spring of fresh, sparkling water bubbled from it.

Samson knelt to drink, and his strength flowed back into his body.

For what he had done, the Israelites made Samson a judge of the land, and he lived among his own people again. He judged wisely and well. For twenty years the Israelites were at peace with the Philistines.

The Philistines dared not harm the people of Israel now, but they continued to plot against Samson.

The woman Delilah was a Philistine. She was beautiful. Silken black hair framed her oval face; her eyes were like black almonds. Samson's love for her was so great he did not see that her eyes were cruel and her hands greedy.

The Philistines said to her. "Tempt him and find the secret of his strength, and we will shower you with coins of silver."

Greedy for wealth, Delilah said she would try. When Samson came to see her she offered him almonds and purple grapes and wine. "You are stronger than other men, Samson," she said, flattering him. "Tell me, wherein does your strength lie?"

Samson smiled. "Bind me with seven green withes that were never dried. Then shall I be weak as other men." His head was heavy

with food and drink, and he slept.

While he lay asleep, Delilah bound him with the green withes the Philistines brought her. "The Philistines be upon you!" she cried then.

Samson awoke and gave a mighty yawn, and the withes broke and fell from him. And so his strength was not known.

"You have mocked me and told me lies," Delilah chided him. "Now I beg of you, Samson, tell me wherein your strength lies?"

Samson roared with laughter. "Tie me with new ropes then," he said, "and I will be weak as other men."

And they feasted on figs, sweet grapes, and wine. When Samson's eyes closed, Delilah bound him with new ropes. "The Philistines be upon you!" she cried, waking him.

Samson stretched, and the heavy ropes binding him snapped like threads. And so his strength was not known.

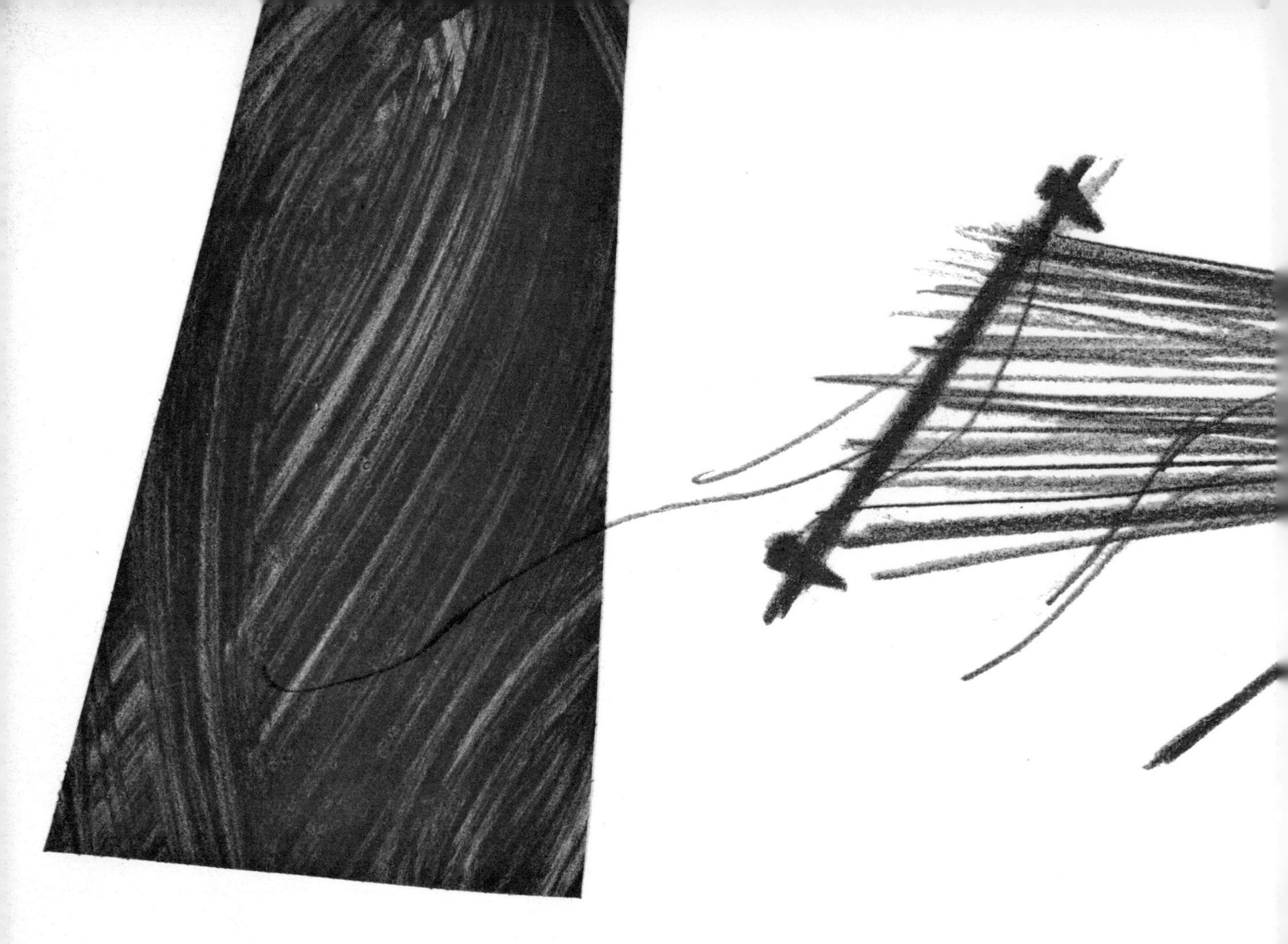

Delilah tried once again. "Since you love me, won't you tell me your secret?" she pleaded softly.

"Weave locks of my hair into the cloth on the loom," Samson told her.

Again Delilah waited for him to fall asleep. Then she worked his long hair into the weaving on the loom.

But when she woke Samson as before, he jumped to his feet and escaped, dragging the loom after him. And so his strength was not known.

"You have mocked me again!" Delilah cried.

Samson dried her eyes. "Do not weep," he said.

And Delilah whispered, "How can you love me if you hide your heart from me?"

Delilah's false, sweet voice rang in Samson's ears. A great weariness came over him. He took Delilah's hand. "Put your hand on my hair," he told her tenderly.

Samson's hair was long and rich to the touch.

"That is where my strength lies," he said. "No blade has ever touched it. That is my secret."

Delilah's face went pale. She saw that this time he had told her the truth. She brought him wine to drink, and he fell into a sleep heavy as death, his head upon her knees.

And Delilah called for the Philistines. "Bring me my silver," she cried, "for I know where his strength is!"

Samson's golden hair fell in gleaming heaps as the Philistines sheared his locks. And Delilah knew she had done him a great wrong. Nevertheless, she cried out, "The Philistines be upon you!"

Samson awoke. I will rise and free myself as before, he thought. But his head was shaved now. His strength ebbed from him, and he was weak as any other man.

The Philistines bound Samson with chains of brass. They put out his eyes and led him away to Gaza.

Blind and alone, he lay in prison and planned revenge.

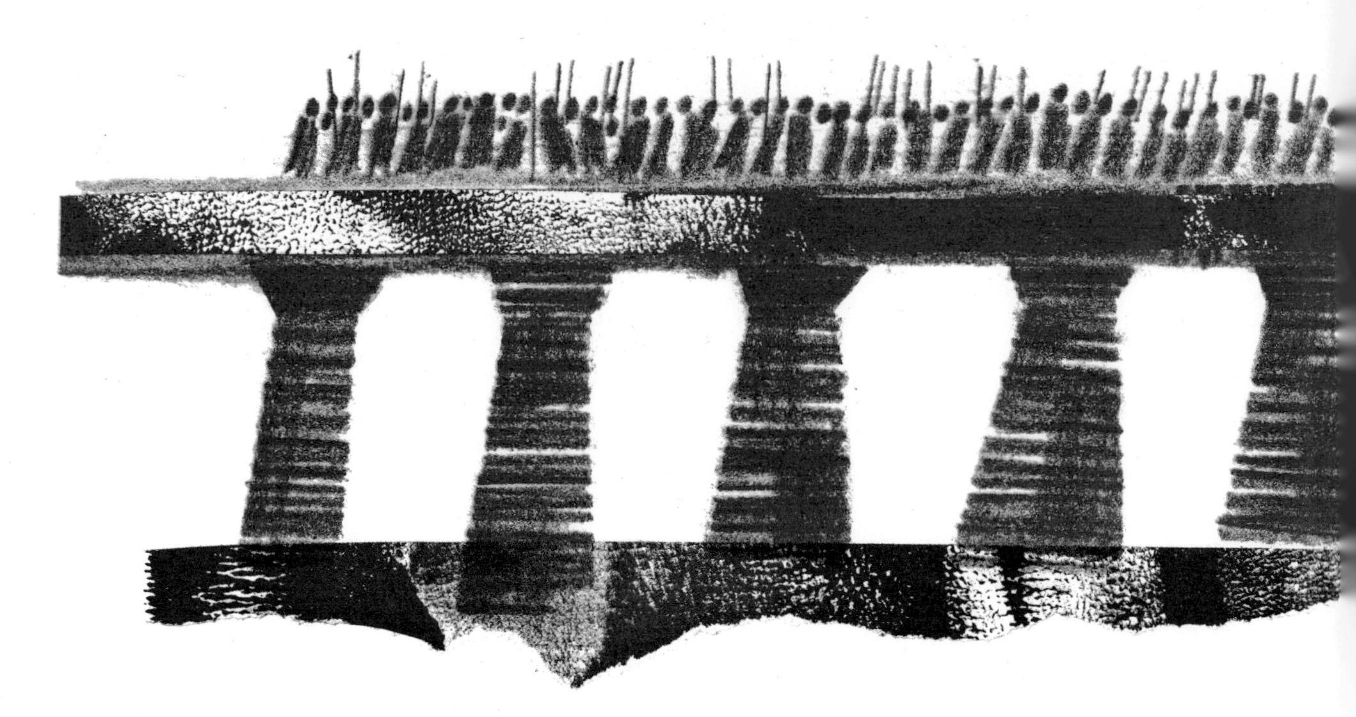

The Philistines believed their god Dagon had rid them of their enemy Samson. In the spring they prepared a great sacrifice in his honor.

Now that he was in jail the Philistines forgot about Samson. Yet all this time his hair was growing back.

On the feast day the Philistines danced around their grinning stone idol. They crowded together at tables laden with meat and olives, honey and almonds, and dark red wine.

The temple was filled with men and women. All the lords of the Philistines were there, and three thousand more people were on the roof.

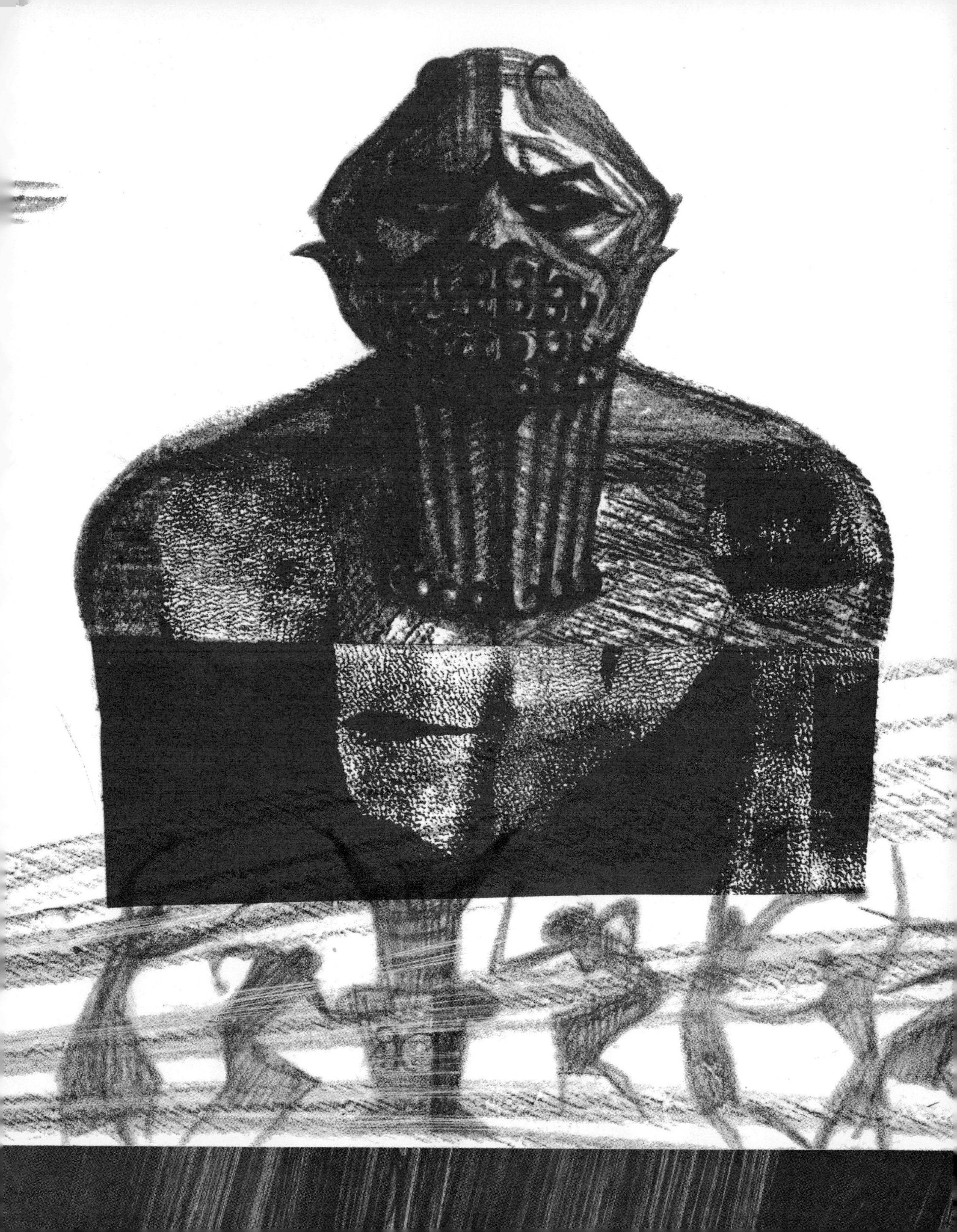

At the height of the feasting, one of the lords commanded, "Call for Samson that he may make sport for us."

Samson was led in and placed between the pillars that held up the building. Blind, and worn with grief, he stood before them. His body was gaunt and stooped now, and his hair, grown long again, had turned gray.

The Philistines spat upon him and mocked him.

As they made merry at his expense, Samson turned to the boy who had led him in. "Let me feel the pillars of this great house," he said, "I want to lean upon them."

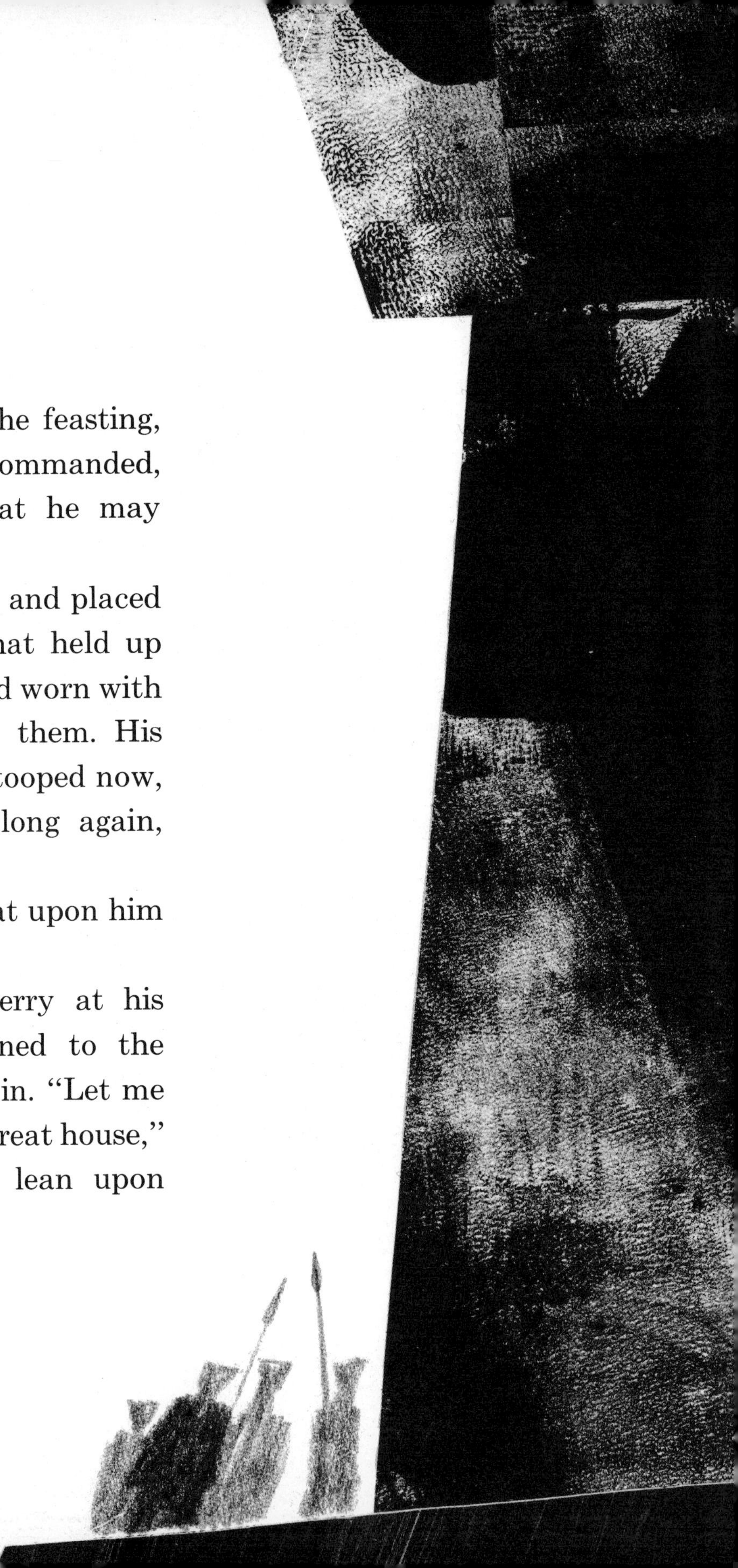

As the boy led him toward the pillars, the jeers and the laughter grew even louder. But Samson did not hear them anymore.

"Oh, God," he called out in a terrible voice, "give me strength one last time that I may be avenged for my two eyes!"

And Samson grasped the two middle pillars that held up the great temple, one with his right hand and one with his left. He bent his back and tugged with all his might.

The ground rumbled and shook. Clouds of dust rose about Samson as the roof caved in and the temple began to fall. Laughter turned into shrieks. The Philistines were buried in the rubble of the temple with Samson, their captive and final conqueror.

And nothing but dust remained . . .

and silence.